Time to Shine
A Daily Journal

Gratitude | Affirmations | Self Discovery

TARA WILLIAMS

This book is dedicated to all the busy, hardworking,
and overwhelmed moms out there trying to be
the best they can be.

You *have to* love YOURSELF first!

It's YOUR time to SHINE!

Introduction

I lost myself for a moment. A long moment…two years to be exact.

Struggling to find balance as an overwhelmed mom, military wife, teacher, and friend, I knew I needed to get back to ME. I just wasn't sure how.

I did know that a morning routine is essential to a successful life. I started small with daily gratitudes and built up to this morning routine.

I knew five minutes was all I could "handle" between getting my daughter ready for school and not being able to sit for long myself. But five minutes was all I needed to change my life. Simple yet impactful.

As a teacher of 20 years, I always knew the importance of goals and objectives. Don't forget to make those measurable…. Oh, and don't forget to track the progress. I did it day in and day out for my students but never for ME. It's time for me to earn my own gold star!

This is your personal journey. Let this book be your guide.
Gratitude + Affirmations / Deep breaths + Self discovery = A NEW YOU!

Get ready to remember who you are, gain clarity to life goals, lower stress, live a fulfilling life, and SHINE!

How to Use This Journal

Everyone has different goals!

Choose one to three goals that you want to work on for the month! The goals can be related to health/wellness, personal growth, money, and so many more! Of course, the teacher in me knew examples were important so I made sure to add examples of Goals, Affirmations, and Intentions for you to use in the following pages. Remember the goal of this book is to be simple yet effective :)

The best part is, if you choose one goal to start, you can reuse this journal for goals two and three :)

So, take five minutes to sit in quiet thought and think about what you want your goal to be for one month! Then write it in the goal page :)

Each day write an affirmation and intention to help achieve those goals. Now affirmations are the act of saying/showing something is true. But the intention is HOW you will get there! HOW you will actually show up! This step is often forgotten but is essential in the process of SHINING :)

Last is Self Discovery—Discovering who you are is a powerful way to create change and build happiness in your life: Let's do this!

Commit five minutes a day to sit by yourself and complete this journal and watch the magic happen! It's time to rediscover who you are and SHINE.

Goals

A Goal is your desired result.

Here are a few examples to get you started.

Health / Wellness / Fitness

✦ I will plan my meals, Monday through Friday, every week.

✦ I will take a 20-minute walk on my lunch break four times per week.

✦ I will be able to do six consecutive pull ups, in the next three months, by training with my trainer twice a week.

Love / Relationships

✦ I will spend 15 uninterrupted minutes per day touching base with my partner to eliminate miscommunication.

✦ I will identify three things I really love about my partner and tell him / her about them on our weekly date night!

✦ I will meet a new life partner by the end of the year by going to an event once a week and meeting new people.

Money

✦ I will pay the outstanding balance of $5,000 on my credit card
and be totally debt free in three months.

✦ For the next year I will save 20% of every paycheck and invest it in a 401K.

✦ I will increase my profits by 20% this year by acquiring two new clients each week.

Success

✦ I will learn something new every week.

✦ I will go to one networking event, every month, for six months.

✦ I will improve my presentation/public speaking skills
by hosting a team Zoom weekly.

Self Growth

✦ I will engage in regular self-care by journaling each morning for five minutes
and taking a bubble bath once a week.

✦ I will develop a higher level of self-esteem and positivity by not sweating the small stuff.

✦ I will read a book every month for the next year.

Write goals here:

GOAL: _____

GOAL: _____

GOAL: _____

Grateful Examples

I am Grateful for:

My amazing family who supports all of my decisions.

My mom and sister for setting great examples for me as a woman.

My mother-in-law for always babysitting our daughter.

My husband for making me laugh daily with his dad jokes.

My strong immune system.

Being able to choose to be a new me whenever I want.

Everyone who has helped me to get to where I am today.

Being surrounded by a loving circle of people.

My business partners for always building me up.

Toilets – indoor plumbing.

My DVR.

Clean comfy sheets and pillows.

Cozy PJs.

Hot tea.

Beverly Hills 90210*

*This should be at the top of my list :)

Self-Growth

Affirmations

✦ I am enough.

✦ Every day I am creating a new and improved me.

✦ Today is going to be a great day.

✦ I have courage.

✦ I have confidence.

✦ I no longer let people's opinion of me affect me.

✦ I forgive myself for my mistakes.

✦ I have the power to make my dreams come true.

✦ I can make a difference.

✦ I am a leader.

✦ I am focused, persistent, and will never quit.

✦ I am in full control of my life.

Intentions

✦ I will look in the mirror and say 3 amazing things about myself.

✦ I will listen to a motivating podcast.

✦ I will shift my thoughts from negative to positive.

✦ I will do one thing out of my comfort zone.

✦ I will hold my head up high and smile.

✦ I will shake off negativity or use it to fuel me.

✦ I will talk kindly to myself and others.

✦ I will celebrate a small victory.

✦ I will help someone today.

✦ I will motivate someone today

✦ I will try something I was previously unsuccessful at again.

✦ I will not have any complaints today. Good vibes only.

Success

Affirmations

✦ I am deserving of success.

✦ I am ready to create the life of my dreams.

✦ I am capable of achieving a meaningful work-life balance.

✦ I excel under pressure.

✦ I am focused.

✦ I have the power to achieve all the success and prosperity I desire.

✦ I work with amazing people who all share my enthusiasm.

✦ Creating solutions comes naturally to me.

✦ I recognize every new challenge as a new opportunity.

✦ I have infinite potential to grow and improve.

Intentions

✦ I will take a step toward learning a new skill.

✦ I will start each day with intention—journal, deep breaths.

✦ I will stick to a schedule – I call it red and green time. Green is GO full speed ahead, and red is family—no work time.

✦ I will take things one step at a time.

✦ I will declutter my digital life and office.

✦ I will show up for myself.

✦ I will host a team-building zoom/party

✦ I will lead by example.

✦ I will show up as my authentic self.

✦ I will set a timer for one hour and work without interruptions.

Money

Affirmations

+ I am a money magnet.

+ I deserve to make more money.

+ I consistently discover new sources of income.

+ The more I give the more I receive.

+ An abundance of money is flowing into my life.

+ I can track my expenses and stick to my budget.

+ My income is always higher than my expenses.

+ Money can show up at any time, in any form, and I am open to that.

+ I make wise financial decisions and trust the process.

+ I control money, money does not control me.

Intentions

+ True prosperity is happiness, be grateful for what you have.

+ I will take one action step to making more money (acquire new client, invest).

+ I will make a plan to pay down debt (Save $100 per week and put it toward a credit card).

+ I will give to charity.

+ I will not buy anything for twenty-four hours (yes, that includes shopping on the internet).

+ I will use what I have – the food, clothes, and gift cards.

+ I will get a new wallet and think of it as a sanctuary.

+ Get yourself a "side hustle," another stream of income.

+ Give someone an amazing tip $.

Health / Fitness

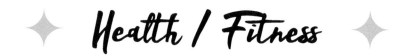

Affirmations

✦ I am healthy and fit.

✦ I am full of energy.

✦ My body grows stronger every day.

✦ My body heals quickly and easily.

✦ My body is the most precious gift.

✦ Everything I eat and drink HEALS me.

✦ I am choosing to prioritize my mental health.

✦ My mind and body are healthy.

✦ I am transforming into a better version of myself.

✦ I am treating my body with respect.

Intentions

✦ I will exercise 30 minutes today

✦ I will only eat healthy foods.

✦ I will lift weights today.

✦ I breathe deeply and fully.

✦ I will rest when needed.

✦ I will drink 70 oz of water today.

✦ I will do something fun for me today.

✦ I will go outdoors, into nature.

✦ I give my body time to recover.

✦ I will eat clean, non-toxic foods.

Love / Relationships

Affirmations

✦ I am worthy of love and deserve to be in a loving, healthy relationship.

✦ I have passion in my life.

✦ My partner and I deserve a long-lasting, happy, satisfying relationship.

✦ My partner and I give our relationship the time and effort it deserves.

✦ I am supportive of my partner, just as he/she is of me.

✦ My partner accepts my flaws and helps me to be a better version of myself.

✦ My partner and I always resolve our conflicts in a peaceful and respectful way.

✦ If I open my heart to love, love will come as I want.

✦ I am a Love Magnet.

✦ My charm is universal.

Intentions

✦ I will allow myself to be more vulnerable today by exposing my feelings.

✦ I let go of control.

✦ I will compliment my partner.

✦ I will set up a date with my partner.

✦ I will hold hands with my partner today.

✦ I will surprise my partner.

✦ I will communicate clearly.

✦ I will introduce myself to one new person this week.

✦ I will be open minded when judging potential dates.

✦ I will focus on having fun.

It's MY Time to Shine!

EXAMPLE PAGE

Gratitude

I am grateful for:

1. My Health
2. Amazing Family
3. Cell phone

Affirmations

1. My partner and I deserve a long-lasting, happy relationship.

2. I am healthy and fit.

3. Money comes to me easily. I am a money magnet.

Deep breaths.

Intentions:

1. I will hold hands and snuggle on the couch with my partner.

2. I will exercise 30 minutes today.

3. I will spend money on things I only need.

Self-Discovery

Look at yourself in the mirror. Give yourself a high-five, and say three things you love about yourself.

1. _____
2. _____
3. _____

SHINE ON

It's MY Time to Shine!

Gratitude

I am grateful for:

1. _____
2. _____
3. _____

Affirmations

1. _____
   _____
2. _____
   _____
3. _____
   _____

Intentions

1. _____
   _____
2. _____
   _____
3. _____
   _____

Deep breaths.

Self Discovery

Look at yourself in the mirror. Give yourself a high five and say three things you love about yourself.

1. _____
2. _____
3. _____

It's MY Time to Shine!

Gratitude

I am grateful for:

1. _____
2. _____
3. _____

Affirmations

1. _____
   _____
2. _____
   _____
3. _____
   _____

Intentions

1. _____
   _____
2. _____
   _____
3. _____
   _____

Deep breaths.

Self Discovery

Write down the name of someone you admire and three qualities they have.

Name: _____

1. _____
2. _____
3. _____

Now cross off their name and change it to your name!
YOU embody those qualities too! It's time to reveal the real you!

SHINE ON

It's MY Time to Shine!

Gratitude

I am grateful for:

1. _____
2. _____
3. _____

Affirmations

1. _____
   _____
2. _____
   _____
3. _____
   _____

Intentions

1. _____
   _____
2. _____
   _____
3. _____
   _____

Deep breaths.

Self Discovery

What does happiness mean to you?

_____
_____
_____
_____
_____
_____

SHINE ON

It's MY Time to Shine!

Gratitude

I am grateful for:

1. _____
2. _____
3. _____

Affirmations

1. _____
   _____
2. _____
   _____
3. _____
   _____

Intentions

1. _____
   _____
2. _____
   _____
3. _____
   _____

Deep breaths.

Self Discovery

Do you forgive others? Let's start with you—what do you need to forgive yourself for? It's OK, we all make mistakes.

_____
_____
_____
_____
_____
_____

SHINE ON

16

It's MY Time to Shine!

Gratitude

I am grateful for:

1. _____
2. _____
3. _____

Affirmations

1. _____
   _____
2. _____
   _____
3. _____
   _____

Intentions

1. _____
   _____
2. _____
   _____
3. _____
   _____

Deep breaths.

Self Discovery

What failure turned out to be a blessing?
That is always when you grow the most.

_____
_____
_____
_____
_____

SHINE ON

It's MY Time to Shine!

Gratitude

I am grateful for:

1. _____

2. _____

3. _____

Affirmations

1. _____

_____

2. _____

_____

3. _____

_____

Intentions

1. _____

_____

2. _____

_____

3. _____

_____

Deep breaths.

Self Discovery

When was the last time you told yourself, and believed,

that YOU ARE ENOUGH?

Today is the day… Say it loud!

"I AM ENOUGH!"

SHINE ON

It's MY Time to Shine!

Gratitude

I am grateful for:

1. _____
2. _____
3. _____

Affirmations

1. _____
   _____
2. _____
   _____
3. _____
   _____

Intentions

1. _____
   _____
2. _____
   _____
3. _____
   _____

Deep breaths.

Self Discovery

If you could change one thing about yourself, what would it be?

_____
_____
_____
_____
_____

SHINE ON

It's MY Time to Shine!

Gratitude

I am grateful for:

1. _____
2. _____
3. _____

Affirmations

1. _____

   _____
2. _____

   _____
3. _____

   _____

Deep breaths.

Intentions

1. _____

   _____
2. _____

   _____
3. _____

   _____

Self Discovery

Name three people who have a positive influence in your life....

1. _____
2. _____
3. _____

Surround yourself with people who feel like sunshine.

SHINE ON

It's MY Time to Shine!

Gratitude

I am grateful for:

1. _____
2. _____
3. _____

Affirmations

1. _____
   _____
2. _____
   _____
3. _____
   _____

Intentions

1. _____
   _____
2. _____
   _____
3. _____
   _____

Deep breaths.

Self Discovery

Name three people who bring negativity to your life...

1. _____
2. _____
3. _____

Why are they still there? Is it time to have a conversation with them?
Or, is it time to take a break?

SHINE ON

It's MY Time to Shine!

Gratitude

I am grateful for:

1. _____
2. _____
3. _____

Affirmations

1. _____
   _____
2. _____
   _____
3. _____
   _____

Intentions

1. _____
   _____
2. _____
   _____
3. _____
   _____

Deep breaths.

Self Discovery

What are you most proud of?

_____
_____
_____
_____
_____

SHINE ON

22

It's MY Time to Shine!

Gratitude

I am grateful for:

1. _____

2. _____

3. _____

Affirmations

1. _____

   _____

2. _____

   _____

3. _____

   _____

Intentions

1. _____

   _____

2. _____

   _____

3. _____

   _____

Deep breaths.

Self Discovery

What are your core values?
Are you living in a way that aligns with those core values?

_____

_____

_____

_____

_____

SHINE ON

23

It's MY Time to Shine!

Gratitude

I am grateful for:

1. _____

2. _____

3. _____

Affirmations

1. _____
   _____

2. _____
   _____

3. _____
   _____

Intentions

1. _____
   _____

2. _____
   _____

3. _____
   _____

Deep breaths.

Self Discovery

How do you feel at this moment? If great, why? If uneasy, why?
And what can you do to change that?

_____

_____

_____

_____

_____

SHINE ON

24

It's MY Time to Shine!

Gratitude

I am grateful for:

1. _____
2. _____
3. _____

Affirmations

1. _____
   _____
2. _____
   _____
3. _____
   _____

Intentions

1. _____
   _____
2. _____
   _____
3. _____
   _____

Deep breaths.

Self Discovery

What advice would you give to your younger self? Do you follow that
advice now? If not, I think it's time to start.

_____
_____
_____
_____
_____

SHINE ON

25

It's MY Time to Shine!

Gratitude

I am grateful for:

1. _____
2. _____
3. _____

Affirmations

1. _____
   _____
2. _____
   _____
3. _____
   _____

Intentions

1. _____
   _____
2. _____
   _____
3. _____
   _____

Deep breaths.

Self Discovery

What is draining your energy? How can you reduce it or cut it out?
Time to say "Bye Bye"!

_____
_____
_____
_____
_____

SHINE ON

26

It's MY Time to Shine!

Gratitude

I am grateful for:

1. _____
2. _____
3. _____

Affirmations

1. _____
   _____
2. _____
   _____
3. _____
   _____

Intentions

1. _____
   _____
2. _____
   _____
3. _____
   _____

Deep breaths.

Self Discovery

What does your ideal day look like? Are you taking the steps to make that
a reality? Choose one thing today to make that happen.

_____
_____
_____
_____
_____

SHINE ON

It's MY Time to Shine!

Gratitude

I am grateful for:

1. _____
2. _____
3. _____

Affirmations

1. _____
   _____
2. _____
   _____
3. _____
   _____

Deep breaths.

Intentions

1. _____
   _____
2. _____
   _____
3. _____
   _____

Self Discovery

How well do you handle stress and anxiety? What can you do to help
with that? Choose one thing today to help ease your stress.

_____
_____
_____
_____
_____

SHINE ON

It's MY Time to Shine!

Gratitude

I am grateful for:

1. _____
2. _____
3. _____

Affirmations

1. _____
   _____
2. _____
   _____
3. _____
   _____

Intentions

1. _____
   _____
2. _____
   _____
3. _____
   _____

Deep breaths.

Self Discovery

In what ways do you show love to yourself?

_____
_____
_____
_____
_____
_____

SHINE ON

29

It's MY Time to Shine!

Gratitude

I am grateful for:

1. _____
2. _____
3. _____

Affirmations

1. _____
   _____
2. _____
   _____
3. _____
   _____

Intentions

1. _____
   _____
2. _____
   _____
3. _____
   _____

Deep breaths.

Self Discovery

What is holding you back in life? How can you change that?
C'mon take the first step....You got this!

_____
_____
_____
_____
_____

SHINE ON

It's MY Time to Shine!

Gratitude

I am grateful for:

1. _____
2. _____
3. _____

Affirmations

1. _____

_____

2. _____

_____

3. _____

_____

Intentions

1. _____

_____

2. _____

_____

3. _____

_____

Deep breaths.

Self Discovery

What is a recent accomplishment you can pat yourself on the back for?
Remember to celebrate ALL wins, big and small.

_____

_____

_____

_____

_____

SHINE ON

It's MY Time to Shine!

Gratitude

I am grateful for:

1. _____
2. _____
3. _____

Affirmations

1. _____
   _____
2. _____
   _____
3. _____
   _____

Intentions

1. _____
   _____
2. _____
   _____
3. _____
   _____

Deep breaths.

Self Discovery

What characteristic makes you unique? Work it!!!

_____
_____
_____
_____
_____
_____

SHINE ON

It's MY Time to Shine!

Gratitude

I am grateful for:

1. _____
2. _____
3. _____

Affirmations

1. _____
   _____
2. _____
   _____
3. _____
   _____

Intentions

1. _____
   _____
2. _____
   _____
3. _____
   _____

Deep breaths.

Self Discovery

What are your five best physical traits? Own it!

1. _____
2. _____
3. _____
4. _____
5. _____

SHINE ON

It's MY Time to Shine!

Gratitude

I am grateful for:

1. _____
2. _____
3. _____

Affirmations

1. _____
   _____
2. _____
   _____
3. _____
   _____

Intentions

1. _____
   _____
2. _____
   _____
3. _____
   _____

Deep breaths.

Self Discovery

Write about the two most beautiful moments you've ever witnessed.

1. _____
   _____
   _____
2. _____
   _____
   _____

SHINE ON

It's MY Time to Shine!

Gratitude

I am grateful for:

1. _____
2. _____
3. _____

Affirmations

1. _____
   _____
2. _____
   _____
3. _____
   _____

Intentions

1. _____
   _____
2. _____
   _____
3. _____
   _____

Deep breaths.

Self Discovery

What does success mean to you?

_____
_____
_____
_____
_____
_____

SHINE ON

35

It's MY Time to Shine!

Gratitude

I am grateful for:

1. _____
2. _____
3. _____

Affirmations

1. _____
   _____
2. _____
   _____
3. _____
   _____

Intentions

1. _____
   _____
2. _____
   _____
3. _____
   _____

Deep breaths.

Self Discovery

What is your superpower?

_____
_____
_____
_____
_____
_____

SHINE ON

It's MY Time to Shine!

Gratitude

I am grateful for:

1. _____
2. _____
3. _____

Affirmations

1. _____
   _____
2. _____
   _____
3. _____
   _____

Intentions

1. _____
   _____
2. _____
   _____
3. _____
   _____

Deep breaths.

Self Discovery

When was the last time you did something for the first time?
What are you waiting for? What is something new you would like to try?

_____
_____
_____
_____
_____

SHINE ON

It's MY Time to Shine!

Gratitude

I am grateful for:

1. _____
2. _____
3. _____

Affirmations

1. _____
   _____
2. _____
   _____
3. _____
   _____

Intentions

1. _____
   _____
2. _____
   _____
3. _____
   _____

Deep breaths.

Self Discovery

Are you afraid of making mistakes even though there is no consequence for it? Why do you think this is? Remember, that is why they make erasers.

_____
_____
_____
_____
_____

SHINE ON

It's MY Time to Shine!

Gratitude

I am grateful for:

1. _____
2. _____
3. _____

Affirmations

1. _____
   _____
2. _____
   _____
3. _____
   _____

Intentions

1. _____
   _____
2. _____
   _____
3. _____
   _____

Deep breaths.

Self Discovery

What is your biggest fear? How has that hindered you?
How can you overcome that?

_____
_____
_____
_____
_____

SHINE ON

It's MY Time to Shine!

Gratitude

I am grateful for:

1. _____

2. _____

3. _____

Affirmations

1. _____

   _____

2. _____

   _____

3. _____

   _____

Intentions

1. _____

   _____

2. _____

   _____

3. _____

   _____

Deep breaths.

Self Discovery

What limiting beliefs do you have? Write down 2 and then ask yourself…Is this actually true? Is there evidence to back this up? If not burn that belief!

1. _____

   _____

2. _____

   _____

SHINE ON

It's MY Time to Shine!

Gratitude

I am grateful for:

1. _____
2. _____
3. _____

Affirmations

1. _____
   _____
2. _____
   _____
3. _____
   _____

Intentions

1. _____
   _____
2. _____
   _____
3. _____
   _____

Deep breaths.

Self Discovery

What have you learned most about yourself in these last 30 days?

_____
_____
_____
_____
_____
_____

SHINE ON

41

It's MY Time to Shine!

Gratitude

I am grateful for:

1. _____
2. _____
3. _____

Affirmations

1. _____
   _____
2. _____
   _____
3. _____
   _____

Intentions

1. _____
   _____
2. _____
   _____
3. _____
   _____

Deep breaths.

Self Discovery

Write a love letter to yourself.

_____
_____
_____
_____
_____
_____

SHINE ON

YOU DID IT! How do you feel?
Take some time to reflect and write how you feel.

_____

_____

_____

_____

_____

_____

_____

_____

_____

_____

_____

_____

_____

This morning routine should be more of a habit now and much easier to maintain. Try it again with another Goal next month. Even if you didn't reach that last goal, did you grow? Did you learn something?
If yes then it's a WIN!

Shining takes time, but five minutes a day is all you need to get started!
You matter! Choose to make the rest of your life, the best of your life!

"Your work is to discover who you are

and then with all your heart

give your light to the world."

—Jennifer Williamson

Take Notes

Take Notes

About the Author

Tara Williams is a jack of all trades but a master of one: helping people shine. As a mother, military wife, teacher, empowerment coach, and business strategist Tara is one busy woman. She began writing children's books when she was an educator. Tara is the author of *Angel Friends* and *Let Your Smile Shine*. She has a passion for journals and created this workbook with the goal to make your life better—easier, calmer, more intentional.

She believes that daily gratitude, manifestations, and a healthy mindset opens the door to living an abundantly fulfilling life!

Tara lives in Rhode Island with her husband Chris, daughter Aria, and their dog Bentley.

CPSIA information can be obtained
at www.ICGtesting.com
Printed in the USA
BVHW020808160522
637113BV00004B/5